Greyfriars Bobby

CORBIE

Text by David Ross
Illustrated by Virginia Gray

© 2001 Waverley Books Ltd
Reprinted 2002, 2004 (twice), 2006

Published by Waverley Books Ltd
New Lanark, Scotland

ISBN 10: 1 902407 16 4
ISBN 13: 978 1 902407 16 6

Printed and bound in UAE

Greyfriars Bobby

In the middle of the city of Edinburgh, by the side of a busy road, stands a red stone column with a drinking fountain for people and another at pavement level for dogs. On its top, there is a small statue – a very small but very famous statue. It shows a little dog, a Skye terrier. He was once just known as "Bobby", but today he is called "Greyfriars Bobby".

The little figure is so lifelike, it is easy to imagine that one day, when no one is looking at him but you, his eyes might open, his little short tail might wag, and he might spring down from his stone column and lead you a merry dance through the old streets of Edinburgh that he once knew so well. And, if he could, he would tell you the story of his life.

Greyfriars Bobby was a city dog. He had been born on a farm out in the country but all he could remember were city streets. Skye terriers were useful dogs. They could hunt rats and other small animals. Bobby was also a working dog. He went everywhere with his master, Jock Gray, a policeman. That's where his name came from.

Policemen were called "bobbies" after Sir Robert Peel, the Prime Minister who set up the modern police force. So what better name for a little police dog than Bobby? The little terrier, so lively and bright-eyed, was also fierce and fearless. Jock Gray had trained him well. Often he had to hold a criminal against a wall, growling and snapping, while his master struggled with another man.

Bobby soon realised that he had a special position and walked proudly along the pavement by his master's side. Jock Gray's house was in the Cowgate, a narrow, dark street in a deep narrow valley. In those days, it was swarming with people and lined with ramshackle, old, over-crowded houses. It was the poorest part of Edinburgh and, while most of the people who lived there were honest, there were also thieves and robbers. The policeman had a busy time.

Bobby was well known to everyone. Every day he went on the policeman's beat, through the busy market area of the Grassmarket, along the dark Cowgate and up out of the valley along a street called Candlemaker Row, where the city's candle-makers once had their workshops. At the top of Candlemaker Row was Ramsay's Coffee House. The policeman was not allowed to eat or drink

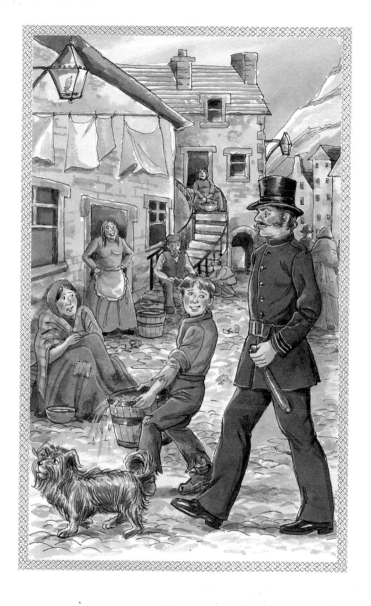

while on duty, but sometimes, after work, he would take Bobby up to Ramsay's and sit by the fire. The policeman's dog was always given a little treat: a bit of sausage, a bannock or a bone. Skye terriers will eat almost anything and Bobby was no exception.

Just round the corner from the Coffee House was a gate that led into a churchyard. A notice in big letters by the gate said:

NO DOGS

This was Greyfriars Churchyard, a green space full of old gravestones around a famous old church. It was a solemn and important place, full of history and carefully looked after by a man called James Brown. It was the only green grass that Bobby ever saw, except when Jock Gray sometimes took him to run on the turf of the King's Park, surrounding the royal palace of Holyrood. Nobody could possibly have guessed that the little dog trotting by the policeman's side would make the old churchyard of Greyfriars into a famous place right across the world.

Jock Gray's work as a policeman, out on the streets in all kinds of weather, patrolling at night as well as in the daytime, was hard. The house he lived in, with his wife and son, was tiny, cold and draughty. He worked very long hours, far longer than policemen do today. And after five years of hard work, he fell ill. He was not an old man, but he was weak from overwork and had to give up his job. Perhaps Bobby missed walking on the beat with his master. But Jock now had more time to take him for other walks until at last he became too ill to go out. He stayed in bed with the little Skye terrier on the floor by him. Jock's illness became steadily worse. The police doctor could do nothing to help him and soon after, he died.

A sad little procession took the policeman's coffin on the short journey from the Cowgate to Greyfriars Churchyard. Jock Gray had been well liked as a fair and honest man and many people stopped work for a minute or two to watch the funeral go by. Men took off their hats and women bowed their heads. Next to the little group of

mourners came scampering a small, bewildered dog. But when they reached the churchyard gate, it was closed before Bobby could go in. Dogs were not welcome. When they came out again, Jock Gray's son, John, took Bobby home. Although he was a police dog, he had belonged to Jock and not to the police force. That evening, as soon as he was let out, Bobby went trotting off up Candlemaker Row, under the tall old houses, until he came to the forbidden gate.

How did he get in? Perhaps he slipped through when someone came out. Perhaps the gate had been left slightly open. Perhaps he wriggled underneath. It's hard to keep a Skye terrier from going where he wants, if he wants to go badly enough. Bobby had any amount of determination. He had been trained ever since he was a puppy to go everywhere with his master and he knew where his master was now. He settled down to spend the winter night by the side of Jock Gray's grave.

He was there in the morning when Mr James Brown arrived to unlock the gate. Mr Brown tried to chase him away. If a dog was seen in the churchyard, people would say he was not doing his job properly. But the little dog would not go. Bobby bared his sharp teeth and growled. Many a

Cowgate villain had felt those teeth in his leg and James Brown decided to leave the dog for the time being. He recognised Bobby as Jock Gray's dog and even brought him out a little bowl of porridge, which Bobby eagerly gulped up.

Mr Brown sent for young John Gray to fetch Bobby away. Bobby would not go but eventually John caught him and carried him down the road. After all, Bobby was his dog now. But Bobby did not see it that way. As soon as he could slip out through the door, he was off, back along the Cowgate and up the hill, to the gate whose notice said "NO DOGS" and, sooner or later, he got back into Greyfriars Churchyard.

"What, are you back again?" said Mr Brown. But he was impressed by Bobby's faithfulness to his dead master and once again he gave the little dog some food.

Bobby also remembered the Coffee House, where he had often gone with his master. Mr Ramsay, the keeper of the Coffee House, knew him well, and Bobby still was given a few scraps of food when he came to visit.

Jock Gray's house belonged to the police force and a few weeks after Jock's death, Mrs Gray and her son had to leave. One day, they packed their few belongings and set off for a new home, far away from Edinburgh. Bobby did not go with them. He was already the dog of Greyfriars Churchyard.

James Brown, the caretaker of the churchyard, soon got used to Bobby being there. He no longer chased the dog away. As he went in through the gate, he looked away from that notice saying "NO DOGS". Not that Bobby spent all his time in the churchyard. Faithful as he was to his master, he would roam around the city, especially in the places where he had once patrolled with Jock Gray. The Grassmarket, with its crowded passages between the market stalls, was always a good place to go looking for tasty scraps, especially near the mutton pie stall. Bobby had no fear of other dogs and was always ready to accept a challenge. His eyes would brighten, his shaggy fur would stiffen, his tough little jaws would open wide to show his sharp teeth and his eager bark would sound. But, luckily for him perhaps, most of the bigger dogs were with their masters and on a leash; and many were muzzled. Bobby could dash in and secure himself a bone or a piece of pie without being harmed.

Another of Bobby's favourite places was the

Castle. Rising high on its steep rock, its walls and turrets towered above the Grassmarket. He had to take a long way round to get in through its front gates. There were always soldiers about, marching up and down, in their tartan kilts. The first time he went there, he may well have followed a pipe band, along with the ragged children who lived in the crowded old houses between the Grassmarket and Greyfriars. Soon the soldiers noticed that they had a regular visitor. Of course, they tried to make a pet of him and would have liked to keep him. A little Skye terrier dog would have made a good mascot for a Scottish regiment. Bobby could have become the dog of Edinburgh Castle and be buried now in the Dogs' Cemetery that you can still see if you visit the Castle. But he always went back to Greyfriars Churchyard.

Every day at one o' clock, the soldiers fired a gun from the Castle walls, so that everyone in the city could tell the right time. (This still happens today.) To Bobby, too, it was a signal. It was time for him to leave his place in the churchyard and come trotting along the pavement to the Coffee House. This now had a new owner, Mr Traill, but he, too, treated Bobby like an old friend, and every day Bobby came down to the Coffee House and

was given a meal. Bobby's mealtime outing happened so regularly that people used to wait at the churchyard gate to see him come out. He was already beginning to be famous.

At night he slept very close to Jock Gray's grave, under a big table-shaped gravestone that was propped up on stone legs. Skye terriers often like to scratch out a bed in the earth rather than sleep in a basket. When the weather was very cold or snowy, he did not sleep there. More than one of the people who lived around the churchyard were happy to take him in. One of these people was James Anderson, who made his living by making and repairing padded armchairs and sofas. His room looked out into the old churchyard. Sometimes, on frosty nights, he would come down and coax Bobby out from under the big flat gravestone and bring him into the warm house. Bobby didn't mind. He knew he wasn't being taken away from Old Jock.

The children from round about also knew Bobby well. But he probably wasn't a very cuddly little dog. He was fierce and proud and used to living by himself. He had long ago chased away all the cats who used to come into Greyfriars Churchyard and, when boys from George Heriot's School came in over the wall from their school-yard, he chased them away, too. But to Mr Anderson and his other friends, he would always wag his stumpy little tail.

A little girl, Helen Dow, who sometimes walked through the churchyard with her father, made friends with Bobby. She would stroke him and he sometimes let her hold him in her arms. He would follow Helen and her father to the churchyard gate and along to the Coffee House. But when they tried to get Bobby to come to their house, he would not leave his place in Greyfriars Churchyard.

Bobby's life seemed secure. But the law said that every dog must have an owner, and every owner must buy a dog licence. The City Council of Edinburgh was worried by the fact that there were many stray dogs in the city streets. The police were told to check on all dogs and make sure they were licensed. Any dogs found to be without a licence were to be caught by the police. They would be taken away and killed.

And so, one day, a policeman came into Mr Traill's Coffee House while Bobby was being given his dinner.

"Gollop, gollop, gollop," went Bobby, paying no attention to what the men were saying.

"Is he your dog?" asked the policeman.

"Oh, no, that's Bobby," said Mr Traill. "He's not mine. I just feed him."

"Who owns him, then?" asked the policeman.

"Old Jock Gray," said Mr Traill. "But he's been dead for five years."

"Very funny," said the policeman.

"I'm not being funny. He doesn't live here. He lives in Greyfriars Churchyard."

"Is that so?" said the policeman. "Then why is there a notice by the gate of that same churchyard which says 'NO DOGS'?"

Mr Traill had no answer to that. He was ordered to appear before the city magistrates for failing to pay for a dog licence.

But before that could happen, the Lord Provost of Edinburgh heard about Bobby and the missing dog licence. A kind man who was fond of animals, he sent one of his officers to bring Bobby to his house. He looked at him closely. Bobby looked back. Lord Provosts, soldiers, schoolboys – they were all much the same to him. Only one man had ever been important to Bobby and that was Jock Gray.

"He's a fine little fellow," said the Lord Provost. "Now, Greyfriars Churchyard belongs to the City of Edinburgh. If that is Bobby's home, then it seems to me that the city must be responsible for him."

And he paid for Bobby's licence himself. A special collar was made. It said "Greyfriars Bobby from the Lord Provost, 1867. Licensed." You can see Bobby's collar today in the Huntly House Museum, in Edinburgh, along with his feeding dish from Traill's Coffee House.

ow his name wasn't just Bobby any more – he was Greyfriars Bobby. Everybody in the city had heard about him. Even in places far away from Edinburgh, some people talked about the little dog who still lived by his master's grave and would not leave it.

Newspaper stories were written about him and artists came to draw him. Visitors to Edinburgh came to Greyfriars to look at Bobby. He was one of the sights of the city, just like the Castle, or the great monument to Sir Walter Scott in Princes Street. It was now nearly thirteen years since the day Jock Gray had died. For all those years, Bobby had maintained his watch by the grave-side.

But he was becoming quite an old dog. Mr Traill and his family looked after him well. But on a winter night in 1872, Bobby's long watch came to an an end, when he died in Mr Traill's house. He was sixteen years old, a good old age for a little Skye terrier.

He was buried close by the church of Greyfriars, and not far from the master whom he had never forgotten. There is a stone there to mark the place.

And outside the churchyard, on that busy street, stands the drinking fountain, with its two bowls, one at ground level, one higher up, to give refreshment to dogs and to people. On top perches the little dog – the very small but very famous, Greyfriars Bobby.

The little figure is so lifelike, it is easy to imagine that one day, when no one is looking at him but you, his eyes might open, his little short tail might wag and he might spring down from his stone column to lead you a merry dance through the old streets of Edinburgh that he once knew so well. And, if he could, he would tell you the story of his life.

And now, you know it.